Millergrams I

Millergrams I

Some Enchanting Questions for Enquiring Minds

by Professor Julius Sumner Miller

1970

DOUBLEDAY & COMPANY, INC., GARDEN CITY, NEW YORK

Library of Congress Catalog Card Number 77–97705

To Alice

PROLEGOMENON or PROLOGOS
or
WHAT THIS BOOK IS ALL ABOUT
and
HOW IT HAS COME TO BE

All of a half-century ago, when I was a little boy on the farm in my native New England, I remember asking all kinds of questions. What is the earth made of? Why is the sky blue? Why is the sunset red? How does a bird soar? Why does a brook gurgle? How does an earthworm crawl? Why is a dewdrop round? Why does corn pop? Why does a wood fire crackle? And a thousand like questions. To a few I got the answers in reading. To some I got the answers in dialogue with my mama and my papa and with my teachers. Some I thought out—not too well, to be sure— but I was learning to **THINK.** By this device—ever questioning—ever uncertain—I gathered up a rather massive body of knowledge.

It is now some fifty years that I have been engaged in this very same gymnastic—asking questions and seeking out their answers. It has all been an extraordinary engagement and it has added abundantly to the fullness of my life— intellectual—emotional—spiritual. It has freed me from the shackles of a fettered mind and it has brought me ever closer to the wonderful things all about us—those things unnumbered which make up the world of nature. At first it was, as Newton said, 'a pretty divertisement.' But now in my later years I see the great virtue it all possesses. First there was the engaging business of gathering up the knowledge—by asking questions—by reading abundantly—by dialogue—by trying to **SEE** when I looked and by trying to **HEAR** when I listened. Now, with a reservoir of knowledge to draw upon, an **UNDERSTANDING** is slowly coming unveiled. It has, you see, taken half a century for this. As I am given to say, lots of people *know* lots of things but our *understanding* is frightfully weak. And before understanding can emerge, a sovereign body of knowledge must exist to draw upon. There can be no meal without the grain to grind.

Now too, I must say a word of another sort. It is this: The human mind is designed for—it has for its purpose most certainly—the intellectual process. This can only be nourished and enlivened by thought and contemplation. There lies, I say, in every human creature what is beautifully expressed by the word *enthusiasm,* which is from the Greek *en theos,* and it means 'a god within,' 'possessed by the gods.' It is this spirit which we all possess but which few ever awaken. Once awakened it grows with unbounded fever and it can drive a boy or a girl or a man or a woman to wondrous things. I have seen it. A tiny spark can set the world aflame and the light of a single candle can pierce the darkness.

Now, how did this book come to be? There are already books no end—big books and little books—the world is full of books—and every one presumably has a message. Homer delivered his beautifully in the *Iliad;* John Locke did it with consummate skill in *An Essay Concerning Human Understanding.* Descartes accomplished it with uncommon strength in *Le Discours de la Méthode.* Plutarch and Chaucer and Rabelais—they all did it magnificently, as did Spinoza and Berkeley and Hume and Adam Smith and Karl Marx and Dostoevski. And you can name a thousand others done as well and still more thousands less ably done. And there are others still, countless in number, of much less pretentious cut, in all the bodies of knowledge humankind has gathered up—exercise books in physics, in

8

chemistry, in everything that people know. But I am going astray! Some time ago one Arnold Earnshaw ('Martin Collins') of *The Australian* in Canberra invited some questions. The scheme was this: A question today, Professor, with the answer tomorrow along with another question. He named the thing MILLERGRAM and I am beholden to him for this new coin. Then came forth the publishers: Let us put your questions in a book, or maybe a series of books. And for this invitation I am further beholden. It is strange indeed that everywhere in the world my questions have had a contagious appeal and this rewards me in an uncommon way.

So there and here our purpose the same—our message the same: some enchanting questions for enquiring minds —for housewives—businessmen—clerks—doctors—dentists— boys and girls and people.

Mindful then of the many pleasures these things have brought to me, incessantly engaged in question, I am delighted to share with young and old alike these exciting adventures. It is as Leibniz put it: 'I hope that others will add the beauty of their minds to the labor of mine.'

So here we have an array of questions on **THINGS**— just things—some simple, some not so, but all, I hope, of an inviting kind. I urge you to engage yourself with a question, bringing to it the passion which living creatures do in abundance possess but which too often lies hidden for want of a proper stirring. You will, I hope, be as was Pascal, 'inflamed with the desire.' The hope I have here is simply summed up: To stir your imagination, awaken your interest, arouse your curiosity, enliven your spirit— all with the purpose of bringing you to ask, as young Maxwell put it, 'What's the go of it?' Or, as Kepler had it, 'why things are as they are and not otherwise.' Or, more simply in my own phrase, 'Why is it so?'

Finally, a word on how to tackle a question. Read it. Read it quietly. Read it out loud to yourself or to someone who listens intently. Get your imagination in gear! Draw a picture in your mind or a real one on paper or on the sand with your finger or with the toe of your shoe. Get into dialogue on it. Use your hands—your arms—gesture—flail them—get excited—show a passion! Find an analogy—what is it *like?* Soon a faint light emerges; the light grows; an understanding comes forth. Soon too the *enthousiasmos*—that divine possession, so long fettered by inactivity—blossoms forth. Leonardo put it well: 'Quiet water becomes stagnant. Iron rusts from disuse. So doth inactivity sap the vigour of the mind.'

And, once again finally, a word of caution! Do not go to the answer until you have felt the joy of your own intellectual gymnastic. It were better indeed that you never had this book if your only purpose is to learn the answers.

Julius Sumner Miller

Millergrams I

Questions

Q 1

You know how very light cork is. When you have a cork stopper in hand—just now taken out of a bottle—it weighs practically *nothing*. If thrown into a bowl of water it floats hardly submerged. The stuff is very, very light. So—quick now—we have a ball of cork—a sphere of cork—5 feet in diameter. Question: What does it weigh? Could you lift it? No calculations! Just give us a quick guess.

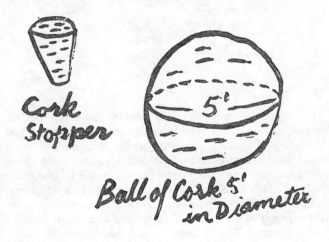

Cork Stopper

Ball of Cork 5' in Diameter

Q 2

A man goes from A to B (however far you like!) at a uniform rate of 20 miles per hour. He returns from B to A uniformly at 30 miles per hour. What is his average rate for the total journey? Be careful now—don't be impulsive! Lots of people get this wrong!

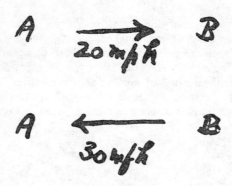

Q 3

The number of molecules in one cubic centimeter of air is roughly 3×10^{19}. Now imagine each molecule to be one grain of sand. So go down to the sea and gather up these grains of sand and pile them into a nice heap. How big a heap do you think you will have? It will be *one cubic mile of sand*—a cubical block of sand one mile long, one mile wide, and one mile deep. Now I want you to count these grains of sand. And suppose you can count them at *ten per second*. This is fast counting! Quick now—how long do you think it will take you to count these? A few days—a month—a year—ten years—a century—a hundred centuries?

Q 4

Consider a wire—such as a telegraph wire—pulled up very, very tight! This wire is very nearly horizontal. I say *very nearly* because it can never *never* be pulled up horizontally. Never—even with all the forces of Hell on one end and of Heaven on the other! So we shall *think* of this wire as horizontal. Now a tiny chickadee lights on the wire. For simplicity it lights in the very middle of the wire between the post supports at its ends. Question: How does the added tension in the wire compare with the weight of this tiny bird? Is the added tension only the weight of the bird— and therefore an ounce or two perhaps?

Q 5

Consider a symphony orchestra. The musicians all tune up at time zero—as we say—before the maestro appears. (And—by the way—by what instrument do they get their proper pitch? Lots of people say, of course, the piano. Is this so?) Now they begin to play. The theater heats up by the people breathing and some sweating—the musicians heat up—the instruments heat up. As a result the instruments get out of tune—out of pitch. Precisely now—what happens to the stringed instruments? And what happens to the wind instruments—especially the metal ones?

Q 6

Let us say that we have a coil spring one foot long—a spring like your screen-door spring. This spring has a modulus, say, of 10 pounds per inch. By *modulus* we mean the force required to stretch the spring—or to compress it— unit length. So our spring requires 10 pounds to stretch it one inch. This is the *force* required to *stretch* it one inch— not the work required! What now is the modulus of half this spring—that is, of this same spring cut in two? (Remember now—half the spring is of the very same stuff as the whole spring.) More generally—if a certain spring of length L has a modulus K, what is the modulus of half this spring?

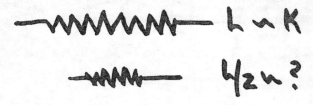

Q 7

Let's have a go at some mirror questions. You stand in front of a plane mirror and observe your image to be as far behind the mirror as you are in front. If you approach the mirror at 10 feet per second, say, at what rate do you approach your image?

Q 8

Consider this mirror business further. You stand in front of the mirror and *move the mirror* toward you at a certain rate, say 10 feet per second. At what rate now does the image approach the mirror?

Q 9

And further on mirrors: A ball rests on the table top— a golf ball, say. You have a mirror in hand. If you rest the mirror on the table top and look into it—with the ball in front—you see the image of the ball. OK? If you roll the ball the image of the ball moves too. Question: At what angle with the plane of the table should the mirror be set so that when the ball moves toward the mirror the image of the ball moves *vertically?*

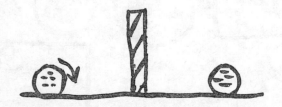

Q 10

Let's go further. Let the ceiling and the two adjacent walls of this rectangular room be mirrors. How many images will you *now* see of yourself?

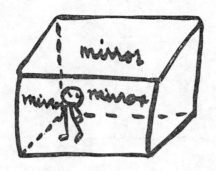

Q 11

Consider a metal plate, uniformly thick, square or circular —like a dinner plate, say—but no ridges—all flat. This plate has a tiny hole in the middle. You heat the plate uniformly everywhere, as by putting it in an oven. Question: What happens to the hole? Nothing? It gets bigger? It gets smaller? Suppose now that the hole were not in the middle but rather off to the side or edge of the plate. What now?

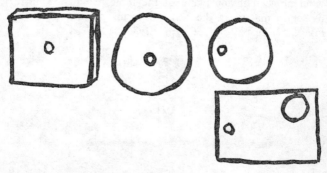

Q 12

Have you not heard the venetian blinds in your windows flutter and hum and vibrate and sing? This happens when the window is open, of course. What goes on here?

Q 13

Don't think I'm done with mirrors! I'm not! I want you to discover how fascinating this exploration can be. Consider two adjacent walls of a rectangular room to be mirrors. You stand in the corner. How many images do you see of yourself?

Q 14

Can a mirage be photographed?

Q 15

In cold climates—in country villages—on farms—farmers often placed tubs of water in their fruit cellars to keep the fruit and vegetables stored there from freezing. At least this is what they said! As a farm boy we did this at home fifty years ago. Is this fiction? Or is there something to it? Is it good physics, let us say?

Q 16

Now finally on mirrors once more: Take two hand mirrors
—the like of which a lady carries in her purse. Place them
so that their vertical edges are together with the mirrors
separated by some arbitrary angle—just like you would
make a kaleidoscope—just like a book opened standing on
its edge. Now place some small thing between the mirrors
so that you see the multiplicity of images in both mirrors.
Play around with this—now bringing the mirrors closer
together—now moving them apart more. You will see that
the number of images depends on the separation of the
mirrors—on the angle between them. At 90° apart there
are three images; at 60° there are five. Got it? Now develop a mathematical expression for these things out of the
observations you make.

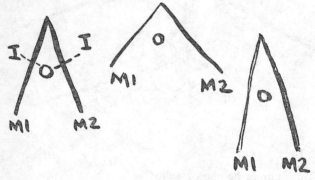

Q 17

On my honour, this is the last mirror problem—for a
while! How tall a mirror do you need to see *all* of you? If,
for example, you are a lady 5 feet 2 inches tall, how tall
—how high—a mirror do you need to buy to see the whole
of you?

Q 18

Rest a yardstick or a meter stick or *any* stick on the outstretched index fingers of both hands. Let the stick be horizontal. Place the stick symmetrically on the fingers. Assume the friction at stick and finger to be the same for both fingers. Now push the fingers *toward* each other smoothly and gently. What do you find? The fingers meet in the middle of the stick. Do you understand this? OK. Now repeat the operation but this time support the stick *un*symmetrically—that is, with one finger say at the 3-inch mark and the other just a little beyond the center of the stick. Now we are to imagine that the fingers are again pushed toward each other as in the first case. Question: Which way will the stick tip?

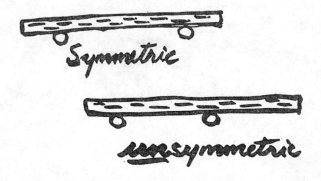

23

Q 19

When a beginner is practising on the violin—or even playing her concert piece!—it is not uncommon to hear a shrill piercing squeak which may be painful to the ear—and to the player—and to the judges! And to her teacher! How is it that this high note arises? There is no string on the violin short enough or under enough tension to give *this* note.

Q 20

You are standing on the edge of the lake watching a fish in the water. The fish is quiet and still—some few feet offshore. That is, you are not looking down on the fish *vertically*. You see him obliquely. If you were to shoot this fish where would you aim? Straight at him? *Below* where you see him? *Above* where you see him?

Q 21

And more on this fish in the water: If you looked straight down into the water—down upon him vertically—would you see him where he really is? Or is he deeper than you see him to be? Or is he less deep? Suppose he is really 6 feet down; where would he *look* to be?

Q 22

Consider a dam built to *hold back* a lake. Must not the dam be 'stronger' for a lake 30 miles long than for one, say, 3 miles long? We assume the water to be equally deep in both cases—at the dam face.

Q 23

Can ice evaporate?

Q 24

What is the interval of time between 1st July, 30 B.C. and 1st July, 70 A.D.? Careful now!

Q 25

A column of troops 3 miles long is marching along a road. An officer rides at a uniform rate from the rear of the column to the head of the column, and back again *at once,* and he reaches the rear of the column just as an advance of 4 miles has been made. How far did the officer ride?

Q 26

Your car is held up by four tires with air in them at a certain pressure. Now jack up one wheel. What's the pressure in this tire now? The same—less—more? That is, is the pressure in the tire one thing with a load on the tire and another without the load?

Q 27

Have you ever observed closely the behavior of smoke coming out of a smokestack or from your neighbor's chimney? On some days the smoke is seen to go up and up into the sky. On other days the smoke issues from the stack and falls at once to the ground below. Why does it do this? **Hint:** You will observe that on dry days it does one thing and on damp days it does the other, and which it does on which days I am *not* telling!

Q 28

A man is carried up an escalator in one minute. He can walk up the stationary escalator in 3 minutes. How long will it take him to walk up the moving escalator?

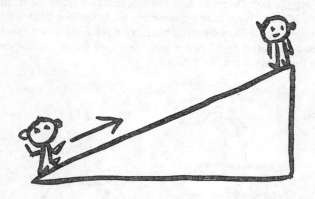

Q 29

If you watch the birds at evening time you will see them demonstrate a remarkable knowledge—better, a remarkable *understanding*—of *physics*. What will they be doing? They are getting ready to rest for the night. They preen themselves, they run their beaks through their feathers, loosen up the feathers all around and fluff themselves up quite big and fluffy. What are they thinking? As an aside: have you heard them sing in the morning and at night? What can you say of *this*?

Q 30

A problem with six wooden matches or six of any other sticks. Take six identical sticks; they must be all the same length. Lay out three on the table top to form an equilateral triangle. This triangle has three sides each equal to the length of the stick. Now we require that with these six sticks you make *four* such equilateral triangles. Remember —the sides of the triangles must be a *whole stick long*.

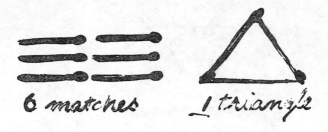

6 matches   1 triangle

Q 31

Some questions on eggs—for housewives and others:

A. Quick now—how can you tell a hard-boiled egg from a fresh uncooked one? And I want it done in a jiffy but *not* by shaking it!

B. Quick now—how can you tell good eggs from bad eggs —*without* opening them, of course?

C. Experiment:
   Spin a hard-boiled egg.
   Touch it.
   It stops.
   Now spin a fresh uncooked egg.
   Touch it.
   It stops—and starts again.
   What's going on here?

29

Q 32

A juggler comes to a foot-bridge of rather flimsy design. He has in hand four balls. The safe load for this bridge is no more than the juggler himself and *one* ball. He solves his dilemma by juggling the balls, always having at most *one* in hand and three in the air. What do you think of his solution?

Quick now—watch the monkey! A ship at sea goes north at 4 feet per second. The tide is going east at 3 feet per second. A monkey climbs the mast at 12 feet per second. What is the velocity of the monkey relative to the Earth?

Q 34

Thermometers may have bulbs—the glass envelopes that contain the mercury—which are either spherical or cylindrical. More usually these bulbs are cylindrical. What virtue does *this* shape have in such an instrument?

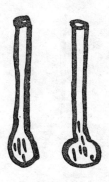

Q 35

Take a wooden match in thumb and finger. Light it by striking it. Can you not hold it in your fingers until it is very nearly burned all away—right down to your very fingertip? Why is it possible to do this? Why don't you feel the heat of the flame?

Q 36

Quick now: which is heavier—a pint of milk or a pint of cream?

Q 37

What do you say to *this?* A ship is slightly lighter when the moon is directly overhead than when it is rising or setting.

Q 38

How can you measure out half a cup of hard, solid butter without melting it?

Q 39

Let us talk about big game hunters. You can read as I have done—somewhere—that 'the bullet knocked the animal clean off its feet'. Or that 'the bullet brought him up all standing'—and such. What do you make of these reports?

Q 40

Let's go back to the tires on your car again. How is it precisely that the air in your automobile tire supports the weight of the car? The pressure, as we say roughly, is only about 40 pounds.

Q 41

Can you drive a paper drinking straw through a raw potato?

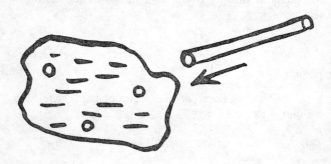

Q 42

The blood pressure of a person is taken (measured) by an instrument called a sphygmomanometer. The rubber cuff part that is inflated is wrapped around the *upper* arm. Why is *this*? Why not elsewhere on the body?

Q 43

When you next visit your dentist or go to a doctor for a throat examination, you will observe—if you observe closely —that the mirror he uses (which is either silvered glass or a good metallic reflector) he first holds closely in his closed hand or in some cases he may put it gently and quickly in a candle flame or a gas flame. Why does he do this?

Q 44

A wheel is rolling with constant velocity along a horizontal road and a piece of mud is thrown off its hindmost point. Do you think the mud will touch the wheel again?

Q 45

And while we are peeling things in the kitchen—how can you peel a chilled ripe, red tomato quickly?

Q 46

Let us say that we are cooking hamburgers in a frying pan or over an open grill. I like to say that to cook them *quickly* you should cook them *slowly!* Does not this sound unreasonable? The fact remains, however, that to cook a hamburger thoroughly in the quickest time one should cook it slowly without the risk of burning it. Why is this so?

Q 47

Quick now—what are the highest and lowest notes employed in orchestral music?

Q 48

If you could approach a stationary sounding whistle with a speed equal to the velocity of sound, what do you think you would hear?

Q 49

For the housewife again: Peeling onions makes some people cry. How can you remedy this? Give at least *three* ways.

Q 50

A man goes from A to B (which is any distance you please) uniformly at 30 miles per hour. Or if you wish, his average rate *for the going* is 30 miles per hour. At what rate must he return from B to A in order to average 60 miles per hour for the total journey?

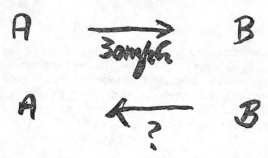

Q 51

Can a ball be thrown in a curve? This throwing-a-ball-in-a-curve business has long been held suspect. Some say it's real —some say it's fiction. What do *you* think?

Q 52

Consider a bucket of water into which you throw at random a cork stopper. The cork will float about one-quarter submerged, since the density of cork is about one-quarter that of water. We wish now to *just submerge* the cork stopper, and for this purpose we must pull it down into the water as by a spring attached to the bottom of the bucket. So now the cork is where it is—just submerged—and it stays here under the influence of the forces down and the forces up. The forces down are the weight of the cork and the tension in the spring. The forces up are the buoyant forces of the water upon it. (Let us consider the spring as being very tiny and contributing nothing to the discussion, save in the tension it provides.) Now—we go to the edge of a tall building and drop the bucket. As it falls you are equipped to observe the stopper with a telescope. What do you see happen to the stopper during the falling of the whole system?

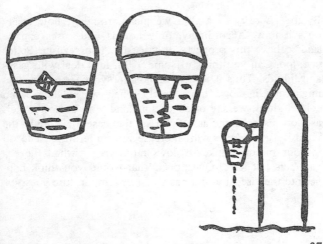

Q 53

It is breakfast time. You are a coffee drinker. Moreover, you use cream in your coffee. You now pour yourself a cup of hot, black coffee. You are *on the verge* of pouring cream into your cup of coffee and it is at this very instant that the phone rings. You wish to answer the phone and return from this to find your coffee as hot as possible. Should you add the cream *before* you leave to answer the phone or should you wait until you return to the table to put in the cream?

Q 54

By the *viscosity* of a stuff we mean, roughly, how freely does it flow. Accordingly, only liquids and gases can be said to have this property of viscosity. **(Correction:** Solids can, too. Can you think of some?) But let's deal with gases and liquids. Thus it is that molasses (syrup)—treacle, you might call it—flows more freely when warm than when cold. Indeed, we say often of someone who is slow: 'He's as slow as cold molasses.' So in the case of liquids the viscosity goes *down* with increase in temperature. The oil in your motor crankcase flows more freely when the engine gets hot. OK? Question: What would you think happens to the viscosity of a gas when *its* temperature goes *up?*

Q 55

Consider the weighing of a body on an *equal*-arm balance. We put the unknown in one pan, say the left one, and balance this with a known weight in the right-hand pan. And the weights are equal and the moments of force are equal. Consider now that we have this body on an *un*-equal-arm balance. You put it, say, in the left-hand pan and balance it with a weight W_1 in the right-hand pan. Then you put it in the right-hand pan and you balance it with a weight W_2 in the left-hand pan. What is the *true* weight of the body? For example, suppose in the one case it weighs 6 ounces and in the other case 7 ounces. What is the true weight of the body?

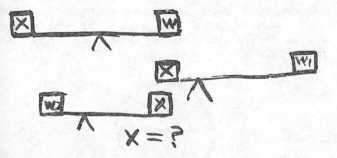

Q 56

The strange properties of rubber bands. *You* call them elastic bands. Are they really *elastic*? And what other very strange properties do they possess? I leave it to you to make some explanation. See what you can discover on your own.

Q 57

In making raisin cake how can you keep the raisins from all sinking to the bottom of the batter—without, of course, making the batter very, very thick?

Q 58

Consider an iron ring or hoop—like an iron tire on a farmwagon. Do we see any of these these days? Across this iron ring as a diameter is fixed an iron rod—by welding it on, say, or heating it on as a blacksmith would do it. Are there any blacksmiths today? The hoop now is a circular ring with a fixed diameter of the same metal—iron. Now we heat this whole business by, say, putting the whole rig in an oven so that all parts are equally heated— more exactly, so that all parts come to the same higher temperature. Question: Does this circular ring or hoop retain its circularity or does it warp?

Consider a small-necked bottle, such as a whisky bottle, which you wish to fill under the water tap—that is, under the water faucet. Why is it easier to fill it by holding the bottle vertically but as far away from—that is, as far *below* —the faucet as is possible?

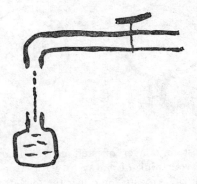

Q 60

Consider two balloons—one filled with hydrogen, the other with helium. Hydrogen is half as heavy as helium. (The density of hydrogen is about 0.0899 grams per liter, I think; that of helium about 0.178 grams per liter—or nearly so.) The balloons are identical in size and are—they exist —in the open air. (The density of air is about 1.293 grams per liter.) Question: How do their *lifting powers* compare? Note that this language is very bad—the balloons do no *lifting,* and *power* is not used correctly—but I cannot write a treatise on the exact use of terms! Does not reason suggest that since hydrogen is lighter it will give more 'lift' and indeed *twice as much* as the helium?

Q 61

The thinnest any layer of stuff can be is *one molecule* thick. Can you think of a way to get a layer of stuff *one molecule* thick? Any stuff in either the solid or the liquid or the gaseous state?

Q 62

We have explored some things that roll—spheres and disks and hoops. They were *solid* spheres, remember. Let us extend our investigations and ask about *solid* spheres racing against spheres that are *hollow*—like hollow balls. A solid ball races a hollow one. What do you predict?

Q 63

The question is sometimes asked: Is the Lusitania on the *bottom* of the sea or somewhere down but *above* the sea floor? Can you give an argument—an unassailable argument—for your position on the matter? And here's an experiment to throw some light on it. Put a *good* egg in a bowl of water. What does it do? It *sinks*—to the bottom. Now add salt to the water. The egg will float? Where? Now with care start over again and have fresh water *on top of* salt water, and lo! the egg can be made to float at the separation—at the boundary. Wonderful to see!

Q 64

When people ask me to speak at some meeting or to lecture or deliver an address they sometimes say: 'Professor, how much time would you like?' To which I reply: 'Well—I do pretty good with a microcentury!' This sure gives them a quandary—a dilemma—a puzzle—which is, of course, just my intention. Cruel—wicked—calculating—all with the intent to make them **think.** So—quickly now—how long do *you* think a microcentury is?

Q 65

If a pot of fat on the stove or the fat in a skillet catches fire, what is the quickest and most prudent way to extinguish it?

Q 66

You can *imagine* this experiment or you can really do it. *Imagination* is a very important ingredient of *thinking!* Let us put a candle in a bottle—vertically upright on the bottom. Fasten it with its own wax to the bottom, if you wish—so that it stays upright. Now light the candle. It burns for certain reasons. Now let us drop the whole business—bottle with candle in it. What happens? That is, of course, what does the candle flame do as the vessel it is in falls? **Nota bene:** Just to say what it does is inadequate. The reason for it doing this or that must be clear. It is not uncommon to get the right result by physically wrong ideas!

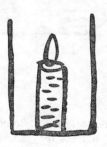

Q 67

Place a slice of hot toasted bread on a cold plate. That is, take a slice of toasted bread out of the toaster and put it on your breakfast plate which has been lying on the table waiting for you. In a few moments water gathers *under* the toast. Have you not seen this? Why is it?

Q 68

In cooking with most pots on the stove it doesn't really matter when you put the pot cover on. But with a pressure cooker, why must you put the cover on the pot *before* you heat the pot?

Q 69

Consider the human heart. What did Leonardo say of it?—'Marvellous instrument, invented by the Supreme Master'. Let us ask a few questions which you can ponder and calculate on. They will reveal wondrous things. How many times *a day* does it beat? How many beats in *a year*? How much blood does each ventricle pump in a day? How much in a lifetime, roughly? How much horse-power can it develop, roughly?

Q 70

Let's look at the waves on the sea. Have you not stood by the sea and watched the waves 'come in'? Why do I use quotation marks on the 'come in'? But let's not get into *that!* So the water wave comes in. If you will observe closely you will see that in general the wave—when still a distance off from shore—is not coming in parallel to the shore—where you are—but rather obliquely. But now as the wave gets very near the shoreline—with one end of it on your left side, say, *nearer* to the shore than that end on your right side—a wonderful thing ensues. The wave straightens out, so to speak, so that it now comes in parallel to the shore. Watch it next time you are there. Now why does it do this?

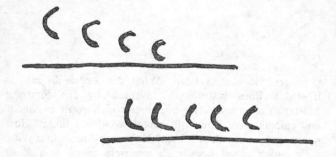

Q 71

You hold in hand a spring scale from which is supported a weight—say of 10 pounds. The scale thus reads 10 pounds. More precisely, the scale reads 10 pounds only under very special conditions: the system must be at rest or moving *uniformly* up or down. You are aware that if the system is accelerated upward the scale will read more and if it is accelerated downward it will read less. This is accomplished by moving the hand impulsively up or down. (The situation has its likeness when you are in a moving elevator. When it starts *up* do not your knees buckle? And when it starts down does not your belly feel empty?) So —you have the scale in hand. It reads 10 pounds. Suppose now you drop it—the whole thing. What will the scale read during the falling?

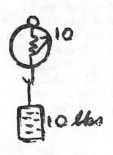

Q 72

A wheel rolls along a horizontal roadway. Is there a point on it which has a velocity *straight up* or *straight down*?

Q 73

Suppose we have three pendulum bobs swinging on three strings. These pendula have lengths as follows: 10 centimeters; 40 centimeters; 90 centimeters. Let's clock their motion. For simplicity count the time for 20 oscillations for each. The times you will get will be roughly these: For 20 swings of the 10-centimeter pendulum, 13 seconds; for 20 swings of the 40-centimeter pendulum, 26 seconds. Quick now—what will the time be for the 20 swings of the 90-centimeter pendulum?

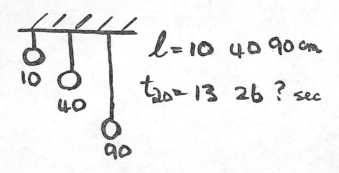

Q 74

Let's talk a bit about rising bread. Why does bread dough rise? If now it has risen and you knead it once again and let it rise again, what results?

Q 75

In northern latitudes in the USA where winters are heavy, as we say, with abundant cold and snow, a man about to buy a home will keep a cautious eye out for a certain event. What does he watch for if he looks at a place to buy? He waits for snow-fall to occur and snow to gather on the roof top. Then as the days go he watches this snow. What is he watching for? What can he learn?

Q 76

Take a clear-glass, flat-sided whisky bottle and fill it *not quite full* of water. Stopper it up, or cap it tightly. Turn it on one of its narrow sides on the table top. What we want to see is a small bubble of air at the upper edge of the bottle. Now grasp the bottle in hand and slide it, say to the right, with a quick impulsive motion. What do you predict the bubble will do? Will it stay still? Will it move in the direction of motion? Or will it move backwards?

Q 77

A very hot iron skillet with an iron handle is on the stove. Why should you not pick it up with a wet dishcloth or wet pot-holder?

Q 78

Blow up a toy balloon. Tie a string to it. Fix the other end of the string to the floor of the car—or just hold the string in hand so the balloon 'floats' in the car. The string is vertical while the car is at rest. The balloon just hovers with the string taut. Now the car is started up. You drive it forward. What does the balloon on the string do? Does the balloon stay right there? Does it go forward? Does it lag behind?

Q 79

The Story of the Three Cans. Take three identical tin cans
—as for fruit juice or the like—and prepare them this way:
Take off the labels. Leave one *shiny*. Paint one *black*—
either dull or shiny black. Strictly speaking, dull black and
shiny black surfaces behave differently but we will disre-
gard these technical details. I say this for those critics who
will complain that I have not said it *all!* Cover the third one
with a *thin* layer of asbestos. Cement it on or fix it on with
a bit of tape. So now you have three cans—one shiny, one
black, one with asbestos. Provide covers for the cans—
small boards will do. And have three identical thermometers. These can be put through tiny holes in the covers.
Now pour into these cans identical volumes—identical
weights—identical masses—of hot water. Water as you take
it from the hot tap, say. Note the initial temperatures,
which should be all alike at time zero. Now let a certain
time elapse. The cans are on your table in your dining
room. The dining room is at a lower temperature than the
cans! After a time, say 20 minutes, the cans have cooled
off—the water has cooled off. So we ask: Which has
cooled the fastest? Which next less fast? Which the slow-
est? Remember your schoolboy physics? Black bodies are
good radiators! Shiny bodies are good reflectors! And all
that stuff. And asbestos is a good insulator. So tell me—in
what order do they cool off?

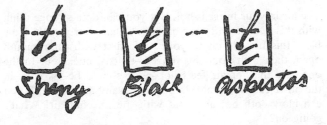

Shiny   Black   asbestos

Q 80

Consider a long glass T-tube with its arms bent downward. To the ends of these arms we fix little glass funnels. To the middle stem we fix a rubber tube so that air can be blown by mouth into the T. Now we dip the ends of the funnels into a soap solution, let a bit of it fasten to the glass edges—and blow into the T. Bubbles arise on the funnels. Now if the arms of the T are in part rubber connections we can control the air that goes into each bubble. So into one we can blow more than into the other. That is, we can blow a *big* bubble and a *small* one. Having done this let us shut off the connection with the outside air by closing the T we blew into. So now we have the two bubbles connected *with each other but not with the outside air*. Correct? So the *big* bubble is connected with the *small* bubble. Question: What now happens?

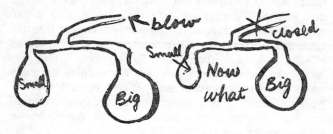

Q 81

The air in your lungs is hot. But you can do a strange thing with this *hot* air. Put your bare arm near your mouth. Now blow this hot air on to your arm, first with your mouth open, then with your lips pursed—that is, puckered. In the one case the hot air feels hot—as it should be—as it is—in the other case it is cold. Is not this really astonishing? You can blow both hot and cold with the one hot air! What's going on?

Q 82

Consider an array of billiard balls in a straight row in contact. Say there are ten. It is best to have them on a V-track so that whatever motion ensues is in the line of the balls. If now one is removed in a line with the others and made to roll upon the nine—the one could be taken *up* the track if the track has a slight bend in it—we see just after impact a very wonderful thing. One goes away on the remote end. Indeed, the *speed* of energy transfer along the line of the spheres is the same as the velocity of sound in the stuff of which the spheres are made. Is not this a wonderful thing! So—one hits; one goes away. Take two up. Let two hit; two go away. *Und so weiter.* We say that linear momentum is conserved. One hitting has mv; one going away has mv. Two hitting have 2mv; two going away have 2mv. (Parenthetically—this matter is all not so simple as I put it—but we will avoid trouble by acceptable simplification.) Question: Let two hit the system at rest. Why cannot we have *one* go away with 2v? Would not *one* m times 2v be 2mv—which is what is required? But if you do this experiment for a thousand years you will never see *one* go away with 2v. I know—I've tried it! And further: We have ten balls on the track. One up—one away . . . two up—two away. Suppose we take seven up and let these seven collide with the remaining three on the track. What now?

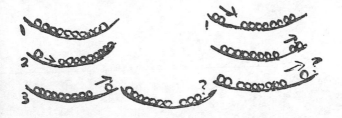

53

Consider a toy balloon. You blow it up by mouth. Make it the size of your head, say. Now you let it go from your fingers and—as Newton so competently said—'The air comes out *this* way and the balloon flies *that* way.' We now ask: What strange behavior of the balloon do we witness? We know that the motion will be erratic but I want more than this. For example, when is the motion of the balloon fastest? Further, the sound arising in the flight of the balloon as the air comes out has a varying pitch. When is the pitch of this sound the highest? Which all suggests that there's more to this than greets the unobserving. And you will be most amazed at the truth.

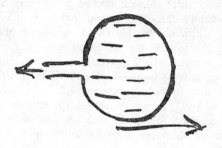

Q 84

There is a story bandied about which goes like this: Some say that ice trays filled with *hot* water will freeze quicker than when filled with water just out of the cold tap. We mean, of course, not the *tray* freezing—it is the water that freezes! What do you think of this?

Q 85

Strictly speaking, the weight of a body weighed on a *spring* scale is good only at the poles of the Earth. Why is this so—and by how much, do you suppose, is the weight different at the Equator? Is it more or less at the Equator?

Q 86

In big supermarkets the merchants have huge freezers—freezing cabinets—along the aisles, in which reside the frozen foods for the customers. The foods herein are often frozen solid. These freezers are *open*. The store itself can be very warm. The freezing elements—the coils that carry the freezing stuff—are often at the *upper* edge of the cabinet; some are also at the bottom. Why is it that these cabinets can be left open without undue 'loss of cold'?

You are an Arctic hunter—and you know a little physics. You go hunting polar bears. You shoot a bear not too far away and you come upon him dead. You have no weighing devices—no scales. You do have a long rope, however. How can you get a pretty good estimate of the weight of the bear? Oh yes—this all happens on very, very smooth ice.

Q 88

A glass vessel—so you can see what goes on inside—has vertical walls—sides—like a laboratory beaker or a drinking glass. This vessel is mounted centrally on a platform which can rotate about a vertical axis—like a turntable. There is water in the vessel. When the turntable is quiet—at rest—the surface of the water is horizontal. This is really an important thing to note. The free surface is horizontal. Now we spin the table. The water in the vessel 'climbs' up the walls of the vessel and a concavity arises in the liquid surface. Of the several possibilities—that is, of the several geometrical shapes which are possible (elliptical—spherical—paraboloidal—hyperboloidal)—what shape does the surface take?

And more on a vessel of water: Let a vessel of water rest on the floor of your car. The car is at rest—still. The water surface is horizontal. Now you start up. You accelerate the vehicle. The water surface *now* does not remain horizontal. Certain measurements on it can give you the acceleration of your car. Can you do this? And when you slow up—decelerate—things happen again. But when your motion is uniform what is the state of affairs?

Q 90

A Paradox of Forces. Take a spring scale. Hang 1,000 grams on it, say; it reads 1,000 grams. Now hang 2,000 grams on it; it reads 2,000 grams. All very simple! Now place this scale on a horizontal platform. Fix strings to its ends. Let these strings pass over pulleys, if you wish, to minimize friction trouble. Now from *each end* of the scale hang 1,000 grams. So now we have 1,000 grams pulling to the left, say, and 1,000 pulling to the right. We ask: What does the scale *now* read? Let me offer you some help! A thousand to the right and 1,000 to the left—aha! the scale reads 2,000. But wait a minute! Instead of *aiding* they may be *opposing*. So it clearly reads *zero!* What do *you* think?

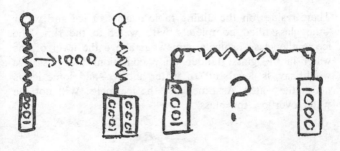

Q 91

How big is a *drop?* When the doctors say 'One drop, twice a day . . . ,' what precisely is meant? Are all drops the same size?

Q 92

There resides on the dining table a glass of ice and water —the glass filled completely with water to the rim. The ice in the glass projects somewhat above the level of the water in the glass. Under these conditions the glass, we would say, is 'level full' of water and ice—and some ice is *above* the water. As time goes the ice melts. Will not the water overflow the glass?

Q 93

And while we are on ice and water: Let's put a thermometer into this glass of ice and water. Let the thermometer read 0°C—or 32°F. The ice melts. Things are 'warming' up, as we'd say. What does the thermometer do?

Q 94

Make a paper dish out of a sheet of writing paper. Fold up the edges—fasten them at the corners. Put water in this vessel. Place it over a gas flame. You can boil the water in the dish without the dish burning up! Or—use a paper drinking cup. Indeed, you can evaporate away—boil away —all the water—*nearly*—without damage to the vessel. How can this be? And, if it is true, why purchase cooking vessels made of metal stuff—that cost money!

Q 95

Why does a flag flutter?

Q 96

In opening a can of fruit juice or the like by puncturing a hole in the can we find that with one hole alone the stuff comes out not so well. So we put another hole in the can. Just why do we do this? **Note:** *You* have done this a thousand times. Right? But I'd like you to *think* about it.

Q 97

Why does popcorn pop?

Q 98

In the game of pool or billiards we have a table with felt covering and an array of balls which are pushed about by collision with others—the *first* one being driven by hitting *it* with a stick. The table is unique in its construction, for the edge of the table—the inner edge—hangs *over* the table surface and has a recess *below* this overhanging edge. The question is: Is this overhanging edge on which the rolling ball collides in any special position? That is, more exactly, how high above the table surface is this edge? How high, I say, in terms of the diameter of the ball? Or is this upper edge of the rim of the table just anywhere? Next time you see this rig look at it more circumspectly.

Q 99

A water wave in the sea—the ocean—having a certain wavelength has a certain velocity. The wavelength is the distance between any two consecutive points in the same phase—that is, for simplicity, the distance, say, between successive *peaks* or humps. So this wave has a very fixed speed. Suppose the sea was now a sea of mercury. What do you think about the speed of the wave now?

Q 100

A wonderful experiment to do with the children—with children aged four to ninety-four! Hard boil an egg. Gently peel off the shell. Into a glass quart milk bottle drop a small burning piece of paper. Let it burn *in the bottle* for a few seconds. Now place the egg on the mouth of the bottle. A wonderful thing is to be seen: the egg gently moves into the bottle. A wonder to behold! What exactly is going on here? *And*—how can you now get the egg *out* without breaking it up?

Q 101

When you walk on dry snow it creaks. What's going on?

Q 102

You reach for a bottle of something that has a metal screw cap on it and you find that the cap is on too tight to remove by hand. This situation is often encountered when a bottle with a metal cap resides in the refrigerator. Quick now—how do you get the cap off quickly?

Q 103

A man stands quietly on a platform scale to weigh himself. Having done this he now *quickly* takes a step to get *off* the platform. What motion of the scale now ensues? That is, does the scale reading at this instant become more—less—or does it remain the same as his quiet weight? Careful now—this needs some contemplation.

Q 104

The Three-Way Spool. Consider a spool like thread comes on. A better one for our investigation here is a big one like wire cable comes wound on. Imagine that you have a wide ribbon wound around the axle of the spool. Now the problem is this: You wish to make the spool do *three* things —you want to make it *roll toward* you—you want to make it *roll away* from you—and you want to make it *slide toward* you. How do you propose to accomplish these ends?

Q 105

Consider this enchanting experiment: Fix a long rope to a very high ceiling or support and at the lower end hang a heavy bob. At the very position of the bob and on the floor stand a pin or a post. The swinging bob is just to clear the floor. Now pull the bob aside and have in mind its swinging as a pendulum. The problem is to push the bob away from you on such a path as to pass by the pin on its forward motion but to knock over the pin on its *first* return flight. How is this accomplished? That is, what path must you give the bob to miss the pin on its forward journey but to hit it on the first return?

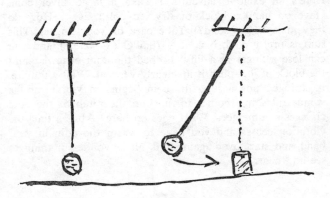

Q 106

A man says to me: 'Professor, what does the Earth weigh?'
To him I reply: 'As much as *you* do.' And then another
man puts the question and I say to him too: 'As much as
you do.' Indeed, I give *this* answer to every man who
puts the question. And I say this is a good answer for a
physicist to give! Can you justify it? **Note:** There are better
answers, to be sure—but I am interested in the validity of
this one.

Q 107

Here's an exciting adventure! Take a large silver coin.
Have on hand a block of dry ice—solid CO_2. (How do
they make a gas solid?) Take care of your fingers. This
stuff is pretty cold; it is at $-78.5°C$ ($-109°F$) and you
can lose a finger in a jiffy. Embed the coin edgewise into
the block of ice—push it in—nearly vertical. Wait a minute.
A strange thing ensues—the coin begins to vibrate and a
wonderful sound comes forth. And the pitch of the note
changes as time goes. What goes on here? After a time the
vibration ceases and you have to warm the coin in your
hand and start over again. It is all a wonderful thing to
see and hear.

Q 108

Fill a bucket with water. Turn on the water hose with the nozzle turned down for a small sharp swift stream. If you feel the hose in your hand when you turn on the water you will feel the hose being *pushed backwards*. This is Newton again. Now insert the nozzle end of the hose *in* the bucket of water. Lo and behold! the hose feels as if it is being 'sucked' further into the water. What's going on?

Q 109

Set up a large electric lamp bulb—100 watts, say—in a socket. Forget the lampshade. It will be in our way. We want the bulb itself—the bare, naked, incandescent bulb. Have the lamp plugged in so that you can energize it in a jiffy by turning on the switch. Now, bare your arm—that portion of your upper arm so sensitive to temperature changes. Hold the naked arm about one foot away from the lamp bulb—the lamp. Now—act quickly—turn on the lamp. At once—instantly—instantaneously—you *feel* the *heat* on your arm. Correct? Quick now—reach over and take hold of the lamp bulb in your fingers. You will find the glass still cold—or at best at room temperature—if it was that to begin. What's going on here?

Q 110

Go down to the seashore. Far off from the water of the sea the sand is dry. Get nearer to the water's edge and the sand is wet—where the sea has receded. Now put your foot down with intent on the wet sand. Now lift your foot. Strange to say, the sand under your foot—the sand which was just now *wet*—is this instant *dry!* And soon the water creeps in again and the sand is wet again. Strange and wonderful thing! What is going on here?

Q 111

I like coarse-grain pepper. Indeed, I like best to grind my own pepper in a pepper-grinder. Let us say that we have a small jar of grain (ground) pepper with a screw cap and holes in the top—so you can shake out the pepper. Let this bottle of pepper reside on the mantel of the stove to be handy for cooking. I have observed that a fresh bottle of ground pepper loses its zip in a very short time—in a few days, in fact. Why is this so?

Q 112

Consider yourself in a warm, cozy bed. Morning comes. It is cold in the room. You throw off the covers and put your feet on the floor. The floor, let us say, is tile or linoleum or marble—or just plain wood. Somewhat removed from the bedside lies a rug on the floor. And what do you do with speed and despatch? You pull the rug over to the bedside with your foot so that now you stand on the rug and not on the bare floor. Why do you do this? Because it is warmer on the rug? But I would remind you that the rug and the floor are at the same temperature since they have been in contact with each other long enough to be, as we say, in thermal equilibrium. Why then does the rug feel warmer? Further to this: If you *have* to stand on the floor—on the bare floor—in your bare feet, what do you do? You turn your foot sideways and stand on its edge! Don't *you* do this? Why?

Answers

A 1

Mirabile dictu! The ball of cork weighs nearly *half a ton!* Would you believe it! Now *prove* it to yourself. It's an elegant exercise in elementary mathematics and it goes to show how deceptive are the volumes of spheres. Which is something to remember when next you buy a grapefruit, say—or a melon. Since the volume of a sphere goes as the *cube* of a linear dimension, a melon just a wee bit bigger gives you much more melon.

A 2

Strangely enough, it is *not* 25 miles per hour! As you may have impulsively thought. Or did you get it right? It is *24* miles per hour. Do you see why? Now prove it to yourself for some arbitrary distance—say 60 miles. Now prove it for 120 miles. Comes out OK, does it not? But proving it for such defined distances is no guarantee at all. There *may* be a distance for which this answer does *not* fit. So the proof must be *general*—for any distance, say D. Try D now and see how *it* fits. So here we learn a method of proof.

A 3

It will take you *one hundred thousand million years!* Is not this absolutely fantastic! And this is the number of molecules in *only one* cubic centimeter of air—which is about one-sixth or less of a tiny match box. So this atmosphere is really something to reckon with. At sea level it exerts a pressure of about 15 pounds per square inch. Nothing much, you say. But let me remind you—you have about 3,000 square inches of surface. This means a load on you of about 45,000 pounds—*over twenty tons!* No wonder you feel exhausted at the end of the day! Imagine the blanket of atmosphere which envelopes the Earth—it weighs 5,000 million million tons. And when it gets going —as in a hurricane or tornado—the energy is something to contemplate. So give these teenie weenzie molecules too small to see and too many to count some proper regard. It is all a wonderful scheme of things.

A 4

The tension in the wire can be thousands of times—millions of times—the weight of the bird! For those who command a bit of mathematics the tension can be shown to be like this: $T = W/(2 \sin \theta)$, where W is the weight of the bird and θ the angle the string or wire makes with the horizon. So if θ is very, very tiny, $\sin \theta$ can be very, very tiny and T becomes enormous. This is why telegraph wires when drawn up very tight—*nearly* horizontal—are in great hazard when snow and sleet gather on them. The added tension can be thousands of *tons*. And the poles and wires go down.

A 5

The strings get lower; the winds get higher. Now an interesting question: The string players can get rid of *their* trouble. *They* can tighten their strings. And next time you go to hear an orchestra watch carefully; they do this with stealth and skill—surreptitiously—so the maestro does not see it! But how can the wind players remedy *their* dilemma? And do you *understand why* the winds get higher? It has to do with the speed of sound. Got it?

A 6

The modulus of half the spring is *20* pounds per inch! In general, if the spring of length L has a modulus K, a spring of the same stuff *half* as long has a modulus 2K. That is, half a spring is twice as 'stiff' as a whole one. Now this is strange indeed—and many a good man has fallen victim to this question. Draw yourself a picture and you'll see why. Better still—take your own screen-door spring and *do* the experiment! Further to this: If two springs were in parallel—each length L and modulus K —we would have a mechanism *twice as stiff*. Now cut these springs—place their halves in parallel—and we have at once a mechanism four times as stiff. Very useful idea.

A 7

Clearly, the image approaches the mirror at the same rate and you approach your image at twice this rate—20 feet per second. Is not a mirror a wonderful thing!

A 8

Is it not amazing that *this* situation should be different! Moving the mirror toward you at a certain rate brings the image upon the mirror at twice this rate. Do this now and see for yourself. It is not at once so obvious.

A 9

The angle is 45°. Try it and see.

A 10

You will see seven (7) images! Isn't this terrific! Now since it might be a job to get a room so equipped, just explore these things on a smaller scale—and have fun.

A 11

The hole gets bigger. Is this what *you* thought? As I like to say—the hole behaves exactly as it would behave if it were filled with the stuff which is *not* there! Sounds crazy, doesn't it!

A 12

Bernoulli's Principle, which is why an airplane can fly—why a bird can soar—why a chimney has a good draught—why a ball can be thrown in a curve—why a boomerang can boomerang—why an aspirator aspirates. The air blows *over* the shutter—a slab of wood or metal with a special geometry. Not unlike in its profile a boomerang. It is curved on its upper side. This geometry is such that the air moving over the upper edge (upper face) gives rise to a reduction in pressure on the upper side, whereupon the atmospheric pressure—now large below—*pushes* the strip *upward*. Now its elastic property or its weight alone brings it down—and the process repeats. This reduction in pressure can be an astonishing matter. In 1938 a huge steel bridge in the state of Washington (USA)—a bridge weighing thousands of *tons* was put into oscillation in this manner. It was torn and twisted in a frightful way and the steel was mangled and the whole bridge torn from its moorings. And in 1949 in Indiana twelve men and women were 'pushed' into a passing train as they stood on the waiting platform and all were killed. Go read about the Bernoulli family: here was a clan of uncommon kind—all 120 of them—all geniuses. No likeness ever in the history of the human race. The Bach family comes nearest, but they were no more than two score.

A 13

You see three (3) images of yourself—and indeed three images of everything in the room. Remember this—it may be useful in another question! Notice how the mirror gives rise to an image of an image and the 'reversal' that ensues.

A 14

Sure a mirage can be photographed. Anything the eye can see the camera can record. The fact is that a mirage is a very real thing. It is not just 'something in your head'. But if you and I look at a mirage we see different things —just as my left eye sees one thing and my right another. Now try and get a photo of a mirage. Have you not come to a rise in the road and when looking ahead at a glancing angle the road looks wet? Have you ever seen the phenomenon called 'looming'? Nature provides deception abundantly.

A 15

It is very good physics. But very, very complicated, really —since water has strange and wonderful properties. As the water cools it gives up its heat energy. When it freezes it gives up more. This heat energy is available then, in the cellar. And, of course, fruits, because of the sugar in them, have a different (lower) freezing point than water. I one time thought—being in my soul a poetic man and emotional—that my papa put those kegs and barrels of water in the cellar to give the little mice some water to drink with their food!

A 16

Roughly, the mathematical expression comes out to be this: $\dfrac{360°}{A} - 1 =$ the number of images—where A is the angle of separation of the mirrors. So it is that for $A = 90°$, $N = 3$; for $A = 60°$, $N = 5$. Now—do all this on paper—locate the successive images and you will discover a beautiful thing. All the images lie on a circle. Pretty thing!

A 17

The mirror must be 31 inches tall. That is, a person can see all of himself in a mirror which is half his height. Notice this strange thing—and maybe it gave you trouble: I did not tell you how far away the mirror is to be. Does it matter? Aren't you glad we're done with mirrors for a while?

A 18

It's amazing, really. The stick does *not* tip. And this again ravages reason. Did you not expect it to tip? If one finger does not move, this does not mean that you are not pushing it. Since forces can exist only in pairs one finger must 'wait' for the other and when friction forces are equal at both fingers—which occurs when they bear equal loads—the fingers move together. Now do this dramatic experiment with a very rough support at one place and a very smooth support at another and the drama is even greater. It is really a wonderful thing to encounter. Engage your friends in this and watch their wonder.

A 19

The squeak arises from the bow being moved—drawn—
along the string—lengthwise—thus producing *longitudinal*
vibration of the string. This results from improper motion
of the bow, which should be only at right angles to the
string. In the question, I spoke of the tension and the length
of the string. What would these have to be, do you suppose,
for such a very, very high squeak to arise with the string
bowed properly?

A 20

Since the fish is *not* where you see him you would miss
him by shooting directly where you see him to be. The
fish is lower in the water than he appears to be. Accordingly
you must aim *below* where he appears to be. Further to
the matter: have you not stepped in to a puddle of water
accidentally to find it deeper than it appeared to be?

A 21

A fish really 6 feet deep in the water would look to be only 4.5 feet down if viewed vertically. How'd I get *this* figure? Now we know what the fish looks like to *you*. Question: How do *you* look to the fish? That is, where does *he* see *you*?

A 22

No! This is a misconception. Many will say—when looking at a great dam—'My! Look at the water that's holding back!' The force on the face of the dam is governed only by the *depth* of water at the face. So—if this be true—let us reduce the length of the lake—keeping the depth constant. We reduce it—to a mile—to half a mile—to a few hundred feet—to a few feet—to a *trickle*. What now?

A 23

Yes—ice evaporates. It has a vapor pressure. Consider this old-fashioned matter: In northern climates—or in southern if you live in Australia—if you hang out wet washing on a very cold day—on a day when the water in the clothes freezes *right now* (and then you get a funny picture of the flannel underwear stiff as a poker!)—the clothes can get dry without ever getting wet again. Wonderful thing, really. The ice evaporates.

A 24

The interval is 99 years. Is this what *you* got? This kind of enquiry can be a bit tricky.

A 25

The officer rode 8 miles. Now there is a strange thing about this problem: you can get the right answer by erroneous logic—if you can speak of logic being erroneous. So be sure your thinking is correct. It is not uncommon for boys and girls to get the right answers to physical problems by thinking which is physically wrong. This emphasizes the importance of *understanding* as against mere *knowing*.

A 26

The pressure is the same—load or no load. Do you see why? Yet one is led irresistibly to think otherwise.

A 27

Strangely enough, damp air—air containing water vapor abundantly—or water in the liquid state—is *less* dense than dry air. Does not this ravage reason! Would you not think that wet air is *heavier* than dry air? Can you *see* why this is so? And so it is that on damp days the smoke comes out of the stack or chimney and falls at once to the ground, since the buoyant forces it can provide are *less* than on dry days. Watch for this. It is enchanting to see.

A 28

It is at once clear that the speed of the escalator is three times the speed of the man. Hence—at once—45 seconds. OK?

A 29

They are loosening their feathers and fluffing up big and loose so as to lodge air abundantly in their feathers and between them. (And is not a bird's feather a wonderful thing to look at!) Since air—still air—air that is quiet—is a phenomenal thermal insulator, birds provide themselves by this device with a splendid blanket over the night. The Wisdom of the Wild. 'Oh,' you ask, 'how do *you* know this is what they are thinking?' To which I reply, 'I have had dialogue with them.' On this insulation business: Throw an angora sweater across your bare arm. *Right now* you feel what the bird feels!

A 30

You have to go to *three* dimensions. Make a pyramid—a tent—a tetrahedron—a polyhedron of four faces—with matches running from the three vertices of the triangle on the table and meeting at a common vertex. Strange that so many are troubled by this when, after all, we live in a three-space world. You ought to explore the *five* regular polyhedra and make models of them out of lucite or cardboard. They are enchanting things to study. The tetrahedron has four faces—triangles; the hexahedron, six faces—squares; the octahedron, eight faces—triangles; the dodecahedron, twelve faces—pentagons; the icosahedron, twenty faces—triangles. There can be *only* five, strange to say. Can you see why?

A 31

A: Spin it about its short axis. If hard, it spins for a long time; if uncooked, it *soon* slows down because of internal motion and viscous friction.

B: Place them all in a bowl of water. Some sink—some float. Which do which? **Note on my philosophy:** It is good not to know all the answers! And I am reminded of the little old lady who did this very experiment and not remembering which did which—bad ones sink? good ones sink?—she threw them all out in despair!

C: Have fun thinking about this one.

A 32

Nonsense! He should learn more about Isaac Newton. As a matter of fact, he makes his chances *worse* by this juggling business. See why? For those who like Newton's Second Law we write $F = mg + ma$.

A 33

Obviously, 13 feet per second. But there could be much more to this problem. What *total* motion does the monkey have?—might be another question to ask. For is not the Earth in *rotation* about its own axis? And is not the Earth in revolution about the Sun? And is not our own solar system in flight toward some distant galaxy (I think it is Andromeda)? It is all a staggering business to contemplate. Just think of it: The total radiation given out by the Great Spiral of Andromeda is 2,000 million times that of our Sun! And this journey about the Sun: once around in 365¼ days—1.6 million miles per day—66,600 miles per hour—19 miles per second. A speed one thousand times greater than that of an express train! A train can go one thousand times faster than a tortoise; so send a train chasing after the Earth—it is like a tortoise chasing after an express train! But more still: the Earth really possesses eleven motions!

A 34

A cylindrical-shaped vessel exposes greater surface, so that the response of the mercury to the thermal energy is more quickly accomplished. Spherical surfaces are, indeed, special designs of Nature—for dewdrops are spherical—as are raindrops. And *watch* the drops of water dripping from your faucet. They 'neck' and drop away, becoming without delay spherical in geometry. Why? Nature wishes to reduce the energy of the system—and a sphere possesses the least surface for a given volume. That is why raindrops are round!

A 35

Wood is a very poor thermal conductor. And the air lodged in the interstices makes it even a better insulator. Thus it is that very little heat energy is conducted—transmitted—along the wood. Interesting fact: conductivity *along* the grain is about three times that *perpendicular* to the grain. Now take a piece of copper the size of a match; hold it by its end in thumb and finger and put the other end in the match flame! You soon drop the thing—right now. Copper has a conductivity 10,000 times that of wood. Now do the experiment with a silver coin; you are doing the very experiment on conduction of heat done first by the Yankee genius Ben Franklin.

A 36

The milk! Nearly everyone says the cream. After all—it's thick and sluggish and viscous. But where do you find it in a bottle of milk? At the top, of course.

A 37

Yes—this is true. Wonderful thing, really. And speaking of the moon I am reminded of our friend Newton again. He often sat—half-clothed—on the edge of his bed—*thinking*. And one time he said: 'I must give up thinking about the moon for it makes my head ache.'

A 38

Fill your measuring cup *half* full with water. Push in the solid butter until the water level rises to the top of the cup. Eureka—Archimedes!

A 39

Nonsense! Pure unadulterated nonsense! What we must say to these utterly ridiculous claims is this. The *forward* momentum of any bullet can be no greater than the *backward* momentum of the gun. More precisely—it is somewhat less by the amount of momentum of the powder. So the bullet can exert no greater impulse (the product of force and time) than the gun exerts on the man who shoots it. Since, obviously, this does not push over the man, it cannot knock over an elephant or a rhinoceros weighing *2 tons* or more! All such declarations are sheer humbug. Now if it's *energy* you think about—the recoil energy of the gun cannot equal the energy of the bullet for if it did the hunter would shoot only once and he would not live to shoot again!

A 40

Let the tire have a pressure of, say, 40 pounds per square inch. We say for brevity 40 pounds. Let us now measure roughly the *area* of contact of the tire with the roadway. Suppose this is 8 inches long and 4 inches wide—give or take a bit. We are measuring that portion of the tire in contact with the road. This area is therefore 32 square inches. This area times the 40 pounds per square inch gives us 1,280 pounds. This is the load supported by *this* tire. *Four* such tires would support 5,120 pounds. So next time you see a mammoth vehicle with sixteen tires you can at once calculate the load it can transport.

A 41

I hope that you have tried this—and found only despair! The straw is generally not rigid enough to take a compression. So it just bends. Now grasp the straw in finger and thumb about 2 inches from one end. Squeeze tight! Tight! Now with a sudden thrust of the hand *drive* the straw into the potato held in the other hand. Presto! It goes right through! Why? The trapped air suffers compression and gives rigidity to that end of the straw. It's a beautiful thing.

A 42

This is the *level of the heart* and hence the problem of hydrostatic pressure is eliminated. The blood pressure could just as well be taken at the ankle—or around the neck. And before we leave this: take a look at that word—see how useful a bit of Latin and Greek can be! Sphygmoma-nometer.

A 43

The mirror—even though at room temperature probably —is at a lower temperature than the air in the mouth or throat. Furthermore—the air in the mouth is filled with water vapor. This is at once condensed out on the relatively cold mirror surface and thus obscures the doctor's vision. So he warms the mirror by some quick action of the hand, which reduces the prospects of condensation. There is some evidence—communicated to me by a doctor —that warming in a *gas* flame 'works better' but I do not too well understand this. What do *you* think of it?

A 44

The mud *will* touch the wheel again as it falls—which is an enchanting matter to contemplate. This suggests at once that the chunk of mud possesses two velocities as it leaves the wheel—but I'll leave the rest to you. Draw a sketch and see why this is so.

A 45

Hold it on a fork briefly—gently—over a gas flame—or submerge it in a vessel of hot water. The skin soon breaks and it is easily peeled off. Now why does the skin break?

A 46

If the meat is cooked *fast* with a high flame, that on the outside becomes scorched and covered with carbon. This carbon coating is a good thermal insulator and it now takes *longer* to get the meat cooked *inside*. On the other hand—there is evidence that the nutritional value of the meat is enhanced by the carbon—but this was not our enquiry.

A 47

The highest note commonly used is the high D of the piccolo with a frequency of 4,702 vibrations per second. The lowest is the E string of the double bass with 41 vibrations per second. Which raises the question of the upper and lower limits of human audibility—another matter for circumspection.

A 48

You would hear a sound with a frequency (pitch) *twice* that of the sounding whistle. This the Doppler Effect. In this case you—the moving observer—move upon the stationary source. Strange to say, if you stand still and the source moves upon you the result is *not* the same! Funny thing—until you explore the mathematics of it.

A 49

(1) Peel them under water. (2) Peel them in a breeze on the porch. (3) Better still: chill them in the refrigerator —or even *freeze* them. This lowers the vapor pressure. So —to be prepared for this event—keep a few onions in the freezer.

A 50

He *cannot* do it! It is impossible! But many say 90 miles per hour. Is this what you said? And I leave it for your further exploration. Do you now see why it cannot be done? Of course, there is a way out—run the course yourself. But I think the speeds required are beyond our competence.

A 51

Sure a ball can be thrown in a curve. Consider a ball in the *right* hand—right as distinguished from left—not right meaning correct! Let it leave the hand rolling along the outstretched fingers. Thus it leaves the hand rotating *clockwise* about a vertical axis *as seen from above the ball*. It will curve to the right looking along its line of flight—as seen by the pitcher. By Bernoulli: A pressure reduction arises (by virtue of the spin) on the *right* side of the ball, whereupon the atmosphere *pushes* it to the right.

More on this: When the batter hits the ball, say, on its *underside*—the underside of the ball—and the ball goes up overhead as a foul and goes *backwards* towards the catcher —the ball on the way *up* spins so that it goes farther backwards towards the fence—but on its way *down* its spin favours a forward drift which now brings it *toward* the plate again. Follow this? These events bewilder the catcher who could do better if he observed the nature of the spin which the ball possesses.

A 52

Since the water cannot exert any buoyant force *during its fall,* the cork is seen to be *pulled down* under the water. In other words—the cork sinks. This experiment is really easy to do. Set it up in a quart glass vessel—climb a ladder near the house—have a number of observers—and you have done for yourself a great classic experiment in the manner of Pascal and von Guericke. It will, I say, stir the spirit of the people.

A 53

You put the cream in *before* you answer the phone. This problem is really very complicated thermodynamically and 200 pages could be written on the physics of it. Which shows that simple matters are not trivial. For our purpose here it is sufficient to say that adding the cream first lowers the temperature of the whole system at once, whereupon the *rate* of heat loss is lessened. That is, the cooler the system to begin with, the *less* fast does it lose its heat. There are at least twenty more parameters—variables—elements —that enter this discussion. Can you name a few?

A 54

Strange thing—the viscosity of gases goes *up* with increase in temperature. See why? Roughly speaking—the higher the temperature of a gas the more chaos in the behavior of the molecules—the more collisions among them—the more sluggishly they move. This is an interesting problem for students of physics, who can show these results either by kinetic theory or on the basis of quantum mechanics.

A 55

The true weight is given by $\sqrt{W_1 W_2}$—that is, the square root of the product. Which makes this $\sqrt{42}$ ounces. This is 6.48 (very nearly). Notice that this result differs from the average, which is 6.5. This simple average is called the *arithmetic* mean; the true weight is given by the *geometric* mean. Do you see *why* they differ and *why* the true weight is not the simple average?

A 56

No—they are not *elastic*. A stuff is elastic if, when it is deformed (within reasonable limits called the *elastic limit*) it recovers its original shape, configuration, geometry. Rubber bands do not do this. If stretched *once* they do not recover their original length. Try it with one. Steel is highly elastic. Glass is highly elastic. Water is highly elastic. Further on these pseudo-elastic bands: Take one in hand—in both hands. Stretch it. Now touch it to your lips. It feels hot. Strange business. Do this again; bring it quickly near a bit of dry paper. The paper jumps up to meet the rubber band. It has become electrostatically charged by stretching. All strange business. Not completely understood. Perhaps you can throw some light on the matter.

A 57

Roll or dust the raisins in dry flour. This increases their surface friction and they will not sink so readily in the batter. (I do not like raisin cakes that have *all* the raisins in the bottom of the cake! They should be equi-distributed.)

A 58

The hoop does not warp. For the same change in temperature the *change* in length is proportional to the original length. Hence the circle expands π (pi) times as much as the metal diameter. Would this be the case if the hoop were iron, say, and the diameter another metal?

A 59

You will observe that when a stream issues from a water faucet and the water falls vertically downward, that the stream *narrows* with increasing distance from the faucet. This is clearly a consequence of the fact that the volume of water in any cross-section remains the same, but since the velocity is increased under the acceleration of gravity, the stream narrows. Accordingly, more water can be gotten into the neck of the bottle more speedily. Further: a *small* stream entering the neck of the bottle permits some space for the air to come out—and there is then no splattering.

A 60

The hydrogen balloon gives *only* 8 per cent more 'lift'.
Is not this surprising!
Argument: $1.293 - 0.0899 = 1.203$
$$1.293 - 0.178 = 1.115$$
Then, $\dfrac{1.203}{1.115} = 1.08$

Hence only 8 per cent more.
And before we leave balloons: *why* do we blow up a balloon? To give it a buoyant force, some would say. To give it buoyancy, some would say. To decrease its weight, some would say. No! We blow a balloon up merely to distend it—so that it will displace some air.

A 61

Drop one teenie weenie drop of oil into a large tray of water. The oil spreads—the film gets larger in area and thinner in thickness—and when it cannot spread any more it is as thin as it can get, which is *one molecule thick*. And you can measure this thickness, too—just do this now. Get the volume of the drop and. . . . Further: watch the beautiful colors.

A 62

The solid sphere will win the race against the hollow one. Over any part of the track racing down hill the times will be in the ratio of 5 to $\sqrt{21}$ — that is, 5 to the square root of 21, which is about 5 to 4.582576. . . . Of course, 5 to 4.5 is good enough! Suppose now that the hollow ball has a *thick* wall?

A 63

The Lusitania is on the bottom of the sea. I'll say no more.

A 64

Very nearly 53 minutes. Just about right for a lecture. Now figure it out.

A 65

Turn off the fire below and *cover* the skillet. This smothers the fire. **Nota bene:** Use of water is dangerous. Water dripping from a wet hand is dangerous. A boiling tea kettle nearby is dangerous. The water vaporizes and spreads the heated fat.

A 66

The candle goes out. Why? Because of the absence of convection. And why is there no convection? Because the air in the vessel has a certain strange property *while falling*. Got it? Recall the cork stopper in the bucket of water.

A 67

However much toasted the bread, the fact is that water still abounds in it. This water is hot water—it may be water in the vapor state locked up in the bread. This vapor is driven out and condenses on the 'cold' plate.

A 68

The pot will expand on heating and then you cannot put the top on. A pressure cooker in the home is a marvellous device. You can cook in a jiffy what would otherwise require many minutes—beets, say. And the *virtue* of the food is not lost to the air. Further: in an ordinary pot you must use abundant water; in a pressure cooker hardly any is needed—practically none—often a spoonful will do.

A 69

Assuming 70 beats per minute—that's 100,000 times a day. That's 40,000,000 beats per year! In a day ventricle pumps about 10,000 liters. That's nearly 11,000 quarts a day! That's about 265,000,000 quarts in a lifetime! With a little calculation that makes it about 140 foot pounds per minute—making it an engine of about 1/240 horse-power. If an elevator could be harnessed to this engine you could ride from the ground floor to the fifth story in about one hour. Marvellous thing to contemplate!

A 70

The velocity of a water wave is a function of the depth of the water in which the wave is propagated. The nearer end then—that end nearer the shore—finding itself in shallower water slows up. The remote end then overtakes it. Needless to say, the friction on the earth-water inter-face plays a large role. The hydrodynamics of this business is rough mathematics.

A 71

The scale will read zero. It is Newton once again—with profound simplicity: $F = mg \pm ma$. When $a = g$, $F = 0$. Which brings to mind a cartoon: Two little boys are jumping off the clothes hamper in the bathroom onto the bathroom scale. Each weighs about 70 pounds. One has landed and he shouts: 'Wow—140!'

A 72

No. Remember question 44?

A 73

Clearly, 39 seconds. Which reveals a very beautiful thing: that the times of oscillation are proportional to the square roots of the lengths. This is revealed by the equation— some call it a formula—for the period of a simple pendulum: $T = 2\pi\sqrt{L/g}$. And just think of it: Galileo discovered this truth by observing the swinging of the Great Lamp in the Cathedral in Pisa as he knelt in prayer at age 17. And he timed the motion with his pulse.

Children—boys and girls—fathers and mothers—do this experiment. The discovery will enchant you.

A 74

The dough rises because of the expansion of the gases which result from the growing yeast. Kneading it once again after it has risen once produces bread with a finer texture because of the more uniform distribution of the gases.

A 75

He watches to see if the snow *stays* on the house roof or *melts* away and disappears in a few days. If it melts away soon the house is poorly insulated.

A 76

Strangely enough—the bubble will be seen to move in the direction of motion—which is what it should do if you contemplate the matter with more circumspection.

A 77

The heat energy from the hot iron handle will vaporize the water and the steam will burn your hand. A *dry* dish-cloth or *dry* pot-holder is safer. Remember—air is a good insulator.

A 78

The balloon goes *forward*. Remember the air bubble in the bottle of water.

A 79

This Story of the Three Cans has a strange and wonderful ending. You will hardly believe it but the asbestos-covered can cools off the fastest. Isn't this amazing! Are you surprised? You should be, for hardly anyone gets this right. And here *I* am in a dilemma. Should I tell you *why?* My philosophy dictates this: I have given you the right answer. *You* must now explore *why* it is right. Nearly all say the black one cools quickest. This is not so. The black one cools *next*. So—go try it—it costs a few cents for the asbestos—very thin stuff—you have the black paint—and the tin cans. If not just eat some canned food—three cans of the same stuff!
Further: this raises the serious question of insulating heating pipes by wrapping them with asbestos. The dilemma deepens. I leave it all to your contemplation and worry.

A 80

Strange and wonderful to witness! Indeed, it can hardly be believed. The small bubble gets smaller and the big bubble bigger. That is, the small bubble blows the big one bigger! Ain't this something! Nearly everyone says: They get equal. And hence we learn about the pressures in the bubbles. Further—when you do this be sure to see the drama and beauty in the colours of the thin soap films. It is a glorious sight.

A 81

This problem involves some wicked thermodynamics. To put it as simply as possible: The hot air undergoes instant expansion when driven out by your puckered lips. This is a cooling process since the work done to accomplish it comes from the heat energy *in* the compressed gas. The air in your open mouth is not under compression and comes out just as it is—hot. The same situation is met when —on a very hot day—after driving far and going fast and hard—you stop to let some air out of your tires, fearing (mistakenly!) an undue increase in pressure. The air is hot outdoors—the air *in* the tire is hot—you are hot—the roadway is hot—the tire wall is hot—yet the hot air coming out *feels cold*.

A 82

Briefly—if one went away with 2v after collision we would *gain* energy—as a quick look at $\frac{1}{2}mv^2$ reveals. And this would violate all of Nature! Now with the seven colliding with the three at rest, *seven* go away after collision. A beautiful thing to see. So—in general—as many go away as hit.

A 83

The speed of the moving balloon is fastest when all the air is pretty nearly out. Isn't this amazing! Wouldn't you think it would be fastest when the balloon is biggest. And the pitch is highest when the *last* air comes out! This all says that the pressure in the balloon is greatest when the balloon is smallest. Would you not say that the bigger the balloon—that is, the more air you put into it—the bigger you blow it up—the greater the pressure in it? But this is not true. Now start blowing up a balloon. Blow it more. When is it the hardest to blow up? OK?

A 84

Nonsense! The cold water freezes sooner—quicker—faster. Obviously the hot water would have to lose its heat energy first—which takes time. Where did this idea ever get born? There is this to be said: The ice which results from the freezing of water is often not clear—but rather cloudy— which is the consequence of air locked up—occluded—in the water. This air is sometimes freed if the water is heated. Thus one can get clearer ice cubes using warm water.

A 85

Because of the motion of the Earth—the rotation on its axis—the body weighs *less* at the Equator by about 1 per cent. Idea: *Buy* things at the Equator—sell them at the poles!

A 86

Because cold air is so much more dense than warm air the cold air in the cabinet *just stays put*. Explore this yourself. In the dead of the night—or any other time—open your refrigerator—I want you in *bare feet*—and wow! The cold air *falls* with a blast down upon your toes.

A 87

Lasso the bear—put the rope around his carcass—move off a distance—pull on the rope. You move—the bear moves too. You measure roughly the distances you each move—you know *your* own weight. At once you have the weight of the bear. OK?

A 88

The surface becomes a paraboloid of revolution. Why do you suppose this is? Consider the forces which act on the wall of water.

A 89

This is a good thing to see. You could use this apparatus as an accelerometer! If the water *slops over backwards* you are accelerating too fast! If you slow down too fast —which may not be bad—the water *slops over frontwards*. What happens on a curve? So you see—it is the angle which the water surface makes with the horizontal that tells you all.

A 90

The scale reads 1,000 grams. Try it this way: You and
your neighbor take hold of the ends of your belt. Let us
say that the tensile 'strength' of the belt is 100 pounds.
You pull with 100 pounds—your neighbor pulls with 100
pounds. Suppose that the belt now breaks. Could *zero*
pounds break it? This disposes of the 'zero' answer—which
many give. Now you dispose of the other. It should be
added that the scale reads 1,000 grams when holding up
1,000 grams *only* when the system is at rest or moving
uniformly up or uniformly down. It is just like being in
an elevator: when it accelerates upward your knees buckle;
when it starts downward your belly feels empty!

A 91

No—a drop is not a drop. The size of a drop is a very com-
plex mechanism. It is governed by the size of the orifice
from which it drips off—by the surface tension of the liquid
—by the geometry of the surface from which it drips—by
the temperature—by the viscosity of the stuff—by the push
of the air which drives it off the end of the dropper—and
other things. Try dripping drops of water and alcohol and
stuff. Close observation will reveal some enchanting things.

A 92

No—the water will *not* overflow the glass. Think of our friend Archimedes.

A 93

The thermometer does nothing. It reads 0°C or 32°F as long as any ice remains. Why? Because the heat energy which the system is taking on goes only into *melting* the ice and *not* to raising the temperature of the system. That is, during change of state there is no change in temperature. As the last vestige of ice disappears Nature now does another wonderful thing: Any heat energy taken on by the system *now does* raise its temperature.

A 94

The kindling point of paper is much higher than the boiling point of water. Hence the heat energy communicated to the vessel and then to the water therein (by conduction) goes into evaporating the water away. And believe it or not: you can boil potatoes in a paper bag! Try it.

A 95

A breeze is blowing. The flag stands out in a vertical plane from the pole. But it is not exactly all in one plane. There is a ripple in it. The air blows by this ripple. If looked at carefully this ripple has somewhat the same shape as an airplane wing. So the air going by gives rise to a reduction in pressure *right* there—whereupon the atmosphere on the other side pushes the flag more that way. But *this* at once results in a ripple on the *other* side of the flag—whereupon a similar effect arises there. And so on. It all depends on Bernoulli again—a reduction in pressure in a constriction where we have fast fluid flow. Note this alliteration—fast fluid flow. And is not a flag a-flutter a pretty thing to see!

A 96

Elementary, Watson! One to let the stuff *out*—the other to let the air *in*. When both try to pass through the hole at the same time, neither wishes to yield to the other. Quite like Robin Hood and Friar Tuck crossing the stream on the log!

Commentary: Many of these events to which I call attention in these questions are commonplace. Indeed, we do them *without thinking*. My crusade is to get people—especially young people—boys and girls—to do more thinking about everything. Whatever it is—wherever we meet it—whenever we see it or hear it—we should ask: **Why is it so?**

A 97

However dry the kernel appears to be—however dry and lifeless—it does contain *some* water. A very tiny bit, to be sure, but there is water there. When heated the expansion is fantastic—enormous—incredible—staggering. And the forces unbelievable. Indeed, one cubic centimeter of water at 100°C becomes about 1,600 cubic centimeters when steam.

More on this lifeless dry inert dead kernel of corn: It seems indeed to be dead. But if put into the Good Earth and given the right heat—the right light—the right dark— the right time—it comes forth with great glory and begets itself thousands of times over. All a wonderful thing to contemplate!

A 98

This overhanging edge is indeed in a very special place. This edge with which the ball collides is exactly seventenths the radius of the ball *above* the table top. Exactly seven-tenths. Can you speculate on the reason for this? Another good problem in analytical mechanics. And important to billiard players.

A 99

Strangely enough—the density of the medium does not enter the discussion. In a sea of mercury, waves of a certain wavelength would travel with the same speed as seawater waves. Is not Nature fantastic!

A 100

This is a wonderful thing to see. Clearly the pressure *in* the bottle gets less than atmospheric and the egg is driven into the bottle. But *why* does it get less in the bottle? Some say the oxygen is used up. This is only part of it. I leave it to you to think about further. As for getting the egg out— a number of wonderful adventures can be pursued. One: Turn the bottle upside down—lodge the egg in the neck of the bottle not quite fitting tightly—blow into the bottle smartly by mouth—get the egg in the neck of the bottle— all this in a jiffy—and presto! the pressure increase inside now *drives* the egg *out*. Can you think of other ways?

A 101

A complicated matter. But roughly this: The 'grains' of snow are moved *over* each other and the friction forces put them into oscillation—into vibration—at a very high frequency, and bodies in vibration give rise to—emit—a wave—which is acoustical. More exactly—the vibrating body gives rise to changes in pressure in the air which impinge on the eardrum which is put into vibration which is conveyed to the inner ear and to the brain. A sound has its origin in a vibrating body.

A 102

All jest aside, a well-equipped kitchen should have an array of Stillson wrenches—small ones for small bottles —bigger ones for bigger bottles—large ones for large bottles. (And incidentally—the *mechanics* of a Stillson wrench—that is, how exactly it works—is a very formidable problem.) But more to our purpose: Hold the bottle in hand with the metal cap in the stream of hot water from the hot-water faucet. The metal—having a higher coefficient of expansion than the glass—expands at once and it is now free to twist off with the fingers. **Note:** This operation can be dangerous if the jar has been in the refrigerator long and is very, very cold. So warm *it* up a bit first.

A 103

Impulsively you would say: Oh, that's easy—the scale reads *more*. This is wrong. The fact is that the man *first* relaxes his muscles in getting ready to step forward or off, where-upon his body 'falls' somewhat and the scale then first reads *less*. Now he *pushes* on the scale platform, where-upon the scale reads *more*. For the physicist, we have:

Case 1: F is less than mg.
Case 2: F = mg + ma.

A 104

What the spool does is governed by the way the pull on the ribbon is done. Take the free end of the ribbon in hand. Now direct the pull in the ribbon toward you but let the ribbon be variously inclined to the floor on which the spool rests. With a little care you will see that the spool wants now to *roll toward* you; a little change in direction will urge it to *roll away* from you; and another little change in the pull will urge it to *slide toward* you. Question: Can you make it *slide away* from you? What the spool does depends upon where the line of action of the pull passes with respect to the point of contact of spool and floor. It is a beautiful exercise in analytical mechanics.

A 105

It cannot be done—as a little contemplation will reveal. For if the bob is sent off to pass by the pin on the left side of the pin, say, then the bob will return to you passing by the pin on the right side of the pin. To accomplish the effect we seek would imply that an ellipse can be made to pass through its own center. I believe this gimmick was one time used in old country fairs. You can still get people to fall for it.

A 106

Since your weight is how much the Earth *pulls you* and *you* then *pull the Earth* equally much, this answer cannot be altogether condemned.

A 107

The heat energy in the coin vaporizes the ice near by its side. The vapor pressure now pushes the coin over to the *other* side of the slot it is in. The melting (vaporizing) action *now* takes place on *this* side of the coin. So—the coin is pushed back and forth. Quite like the classic Trevelyan Rocker which some of you may know.

A 108

It's Bernoulli again. See why? A diminution in pressure *in* the fast stream, whereupon the water around *pushes* the hose further in. Notice that I put the word 'suction' in quotation marks. There is no such action—'suction' does not exist. When this 'feeling' of a certain kind of force exists it means that something elsewhere is *pushing*. There is nothing sucking things in!

A 109

Obviously—the *heat* you feel at a distance is the result of absorption of the radiation emitted by the incandescent lamp filament. This radiation passes through the glass walls quite readily and reaches your arm with the velocity of electromagnetic radiations—nearly all the same velocity for all wavelengths (colours). (The same velocity in free space —to make it exact.) The effect is therefore felt at your arm *before* the glass itself can be heated up. Conduction processes are very slow.

A 110

I do not understand this! It appears simple enough—you *squeeze* the water out under your foot—the grains of sand suffer a packing—they *look* very dry—but this picture is optical and involves the reflectivity of the sand when wet and when dry. You lift your foot—the water rushes back in. But when you really do this adventure some perplexing questions arise. Look into it.

A 111

When we smell something it is the flavor of the stuff that falls on the proper nerves to give us the olfactory sense. So it is that when the 'flavor pressure' is high we smell the stuff better. This is really a *vapor* pressure. This vapor pressure increases with temperature—it is merely a gas—so it is that the pepper being warmed on the stove loses its flavor at a faster rate. Remember the onion in the freezer? And try this adventure: Crush a geranium leaf in the fingers—smell it. Now just warm up a bit of the crushed leaf.

A 112

The bare floor is a good thermal conductor and takes the heat away from the foot—that is, it takes the heat of the foot away. This is what makes it feel cold. On the other hand, the rug has locked up in it in the threads and between the threads much quiet air—and air is a good thermal insulator. And why do you stand on the *edge* of your foot? To reduce the area of contact so that less heat is taken away from the foot.